Published by Dover Publications, Inc., 31 East 2nd Street, Mineola, N.Y. 11501.

Stegosaurus. By Matthew Kalmenoff. © 1985 by Matthew Kalmenoff. Published by Dover Publications, Inc., 31 East 2nd Street, Mineola, N.Y. 11501.

Triceratops and Tyrannosaurus rex. By Matthew Kalmenoff. © 1985 by Matthew Kalmenoff. Published by Dover Publications, Inc., 31 East 2nd Street, Mineola, N.Y. 11501.

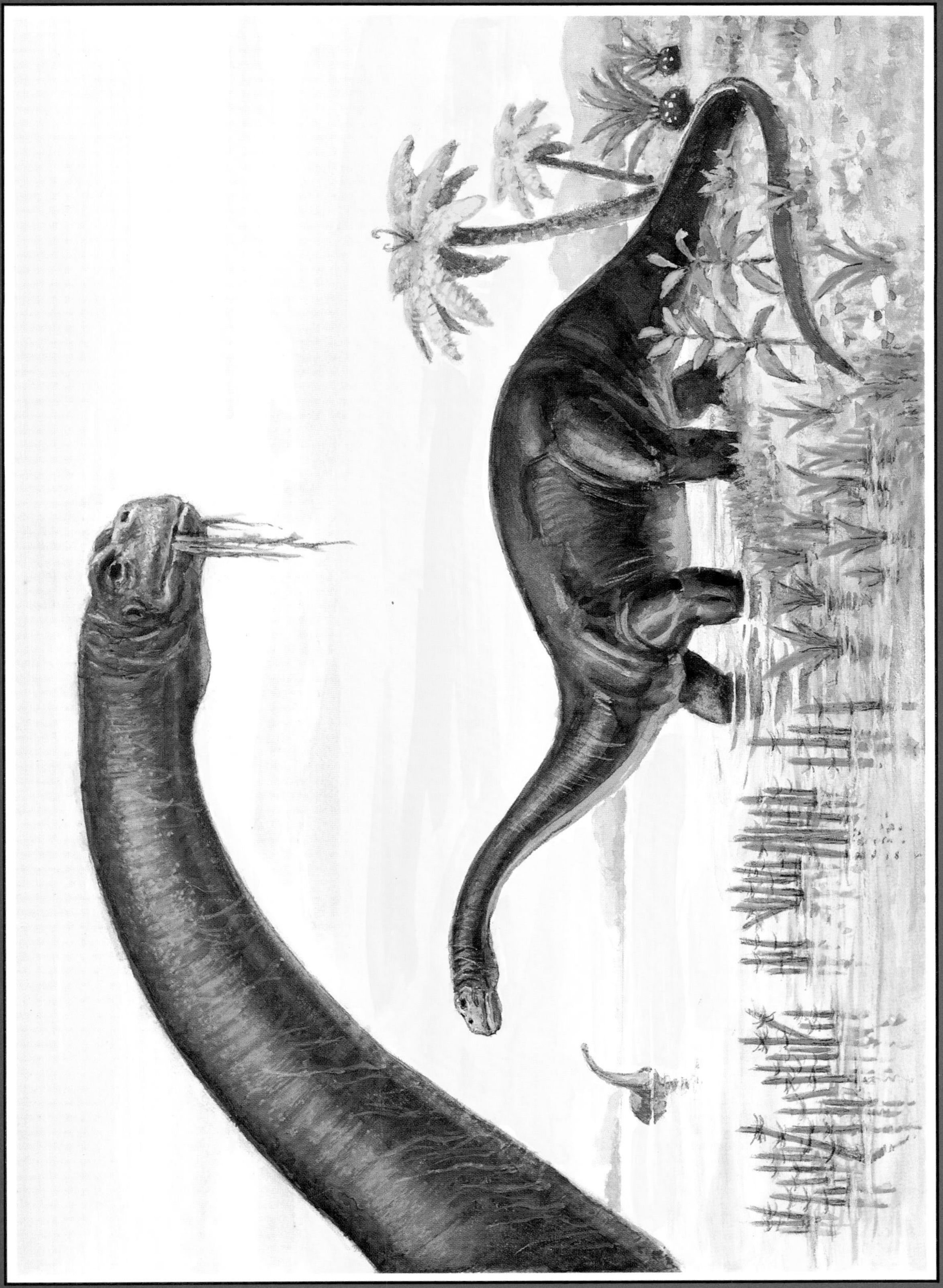